A HEART FOR DADDY

Helping Kids Recover from Parent's Self-Harm

Leticia Murphy, M.A., LMFT
and Sharon D. Walling

Illustrations by Debbie J Hefke

ISBN: 978-1-7333969-4-3

Printed in the United States of America

Empire Publishing

www.empirebookpublishing.com

DEDICATION

This book is dedicated to all the teachers, family, and friends who have been here supporting the little ones left behind; and to the survivors, especially Amelia, Brandon, Cameron, and Devlin.
You all are stronger than you know and loved more than you know.

A HEART FOR DADDY

I went to school today because my mom said it would be good for me.

All I did was stare.

At recess I cried.

My daddy is why I cried. He hurt himself, very badly. His heart stopped beating.

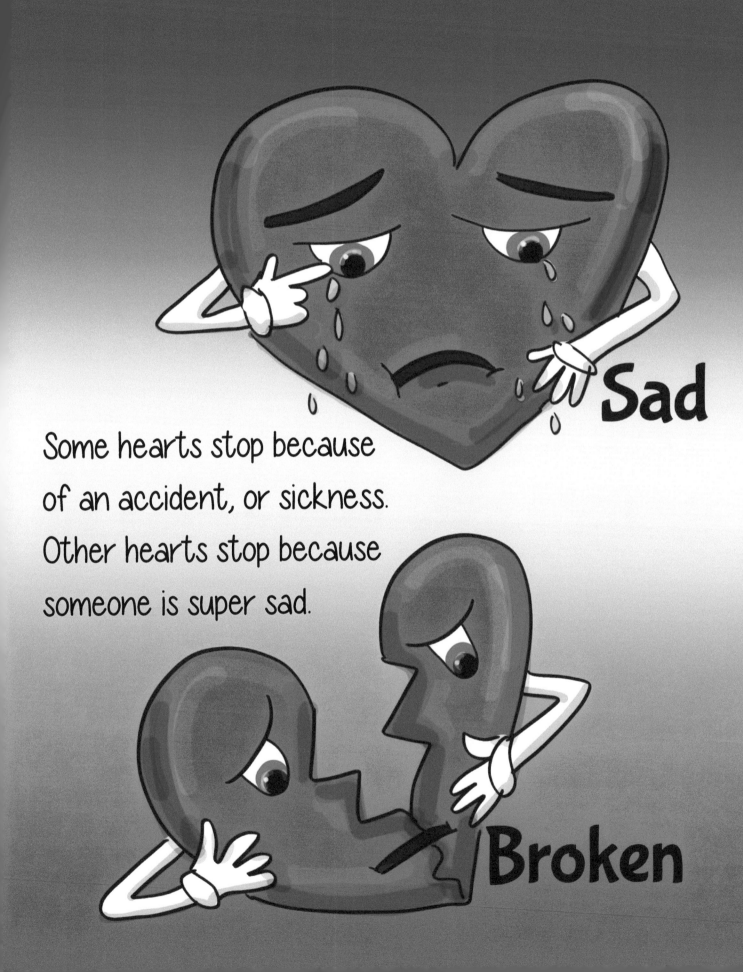

Sad

Some hearts stop because
of an accident, or sickness.
Other hearts stop because
someone is super sad.

Broken

My daddy was super sad and made a decision that was very bad. The one that made him hurt himself.

He didn't think it would hurt me or my mom, or even his friends . . . or our whole family.

I wish he would have gotten help for his sadness. Then maybe he would still be here with me.

I feel alone and scared, and sometimes I have nightmares. I keep imagining he will come home from work, but I never hear his car in the driveway.

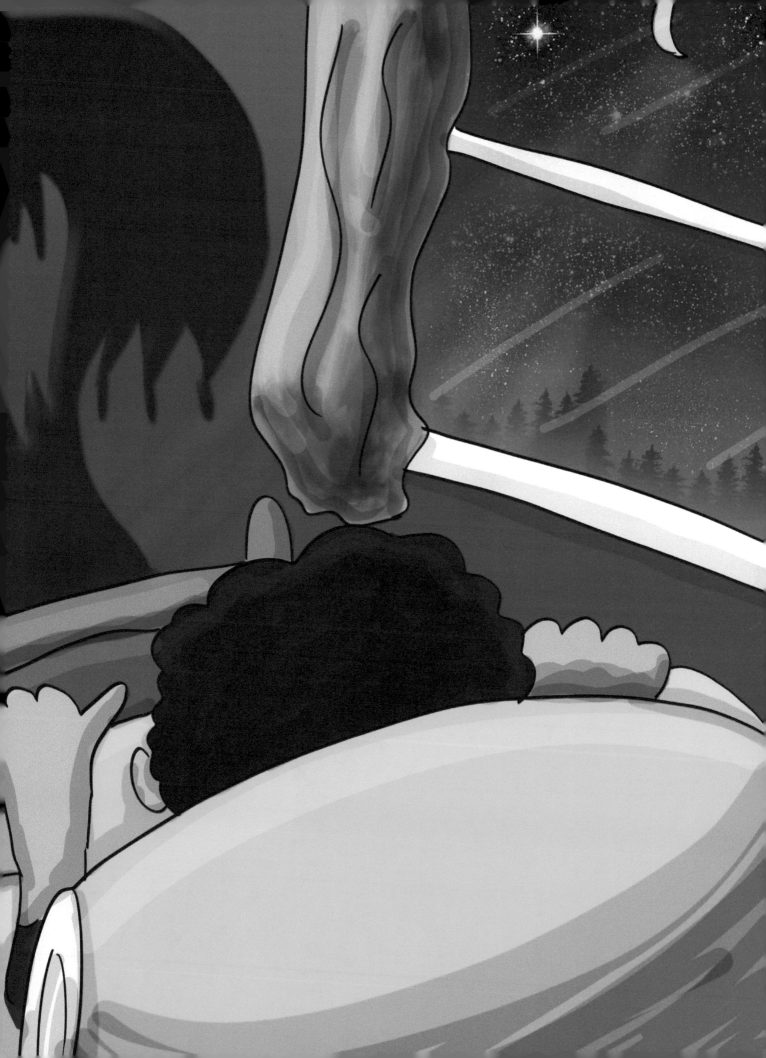

Sometimes, I get really angry that he left us alone.

And sometimes I wonder, did I do something wrong?

But Mom said it is no one's fault.

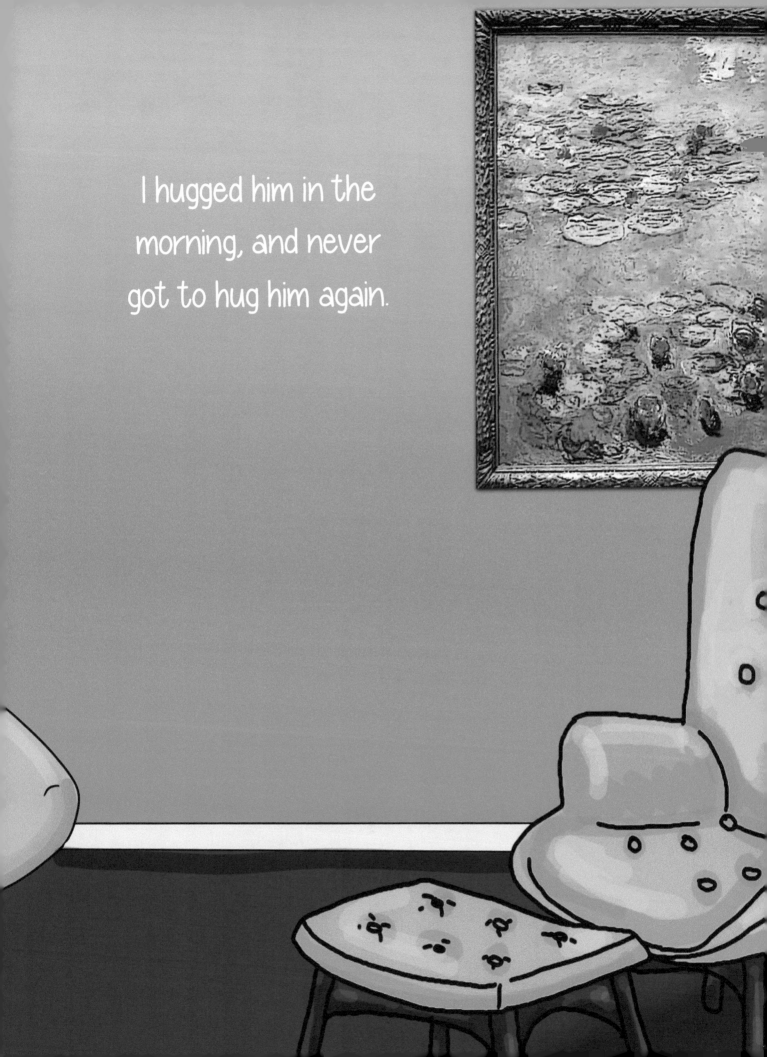

I hugged him in the morning, and never got to hug him again.

I don't like to go to Pancake Carousel anymore. Because we used to go there for pancakes on Saturdays.

I didn't really want to go to school.
But I did.

After school my teacher talked to me.
She said, "I remember your dad, too. He came
to Open House. He was a very nice man."

Then she asked me, "What do you remember most about your father?"

I told her I liked his deep laugh and our pancakes together, how he helped me learn to ride my bike.

She told me I can put my memories in a book, and it will keep him alive in my heart.

My teacher let me cry.

I told her sometimes I cry, then I want to go play with my friends, then I want to go home and be alone again.

My mom told me it's okay. That it would take a while for me to not cry as much. She said, "Daddy loved you very much, but he was very sad. We don't know why he was unhappy."

She said he hid his sadness, so we wouldn't know. But Mom told me, if I'm sad, don't hide it. Tell her so together we can get help.

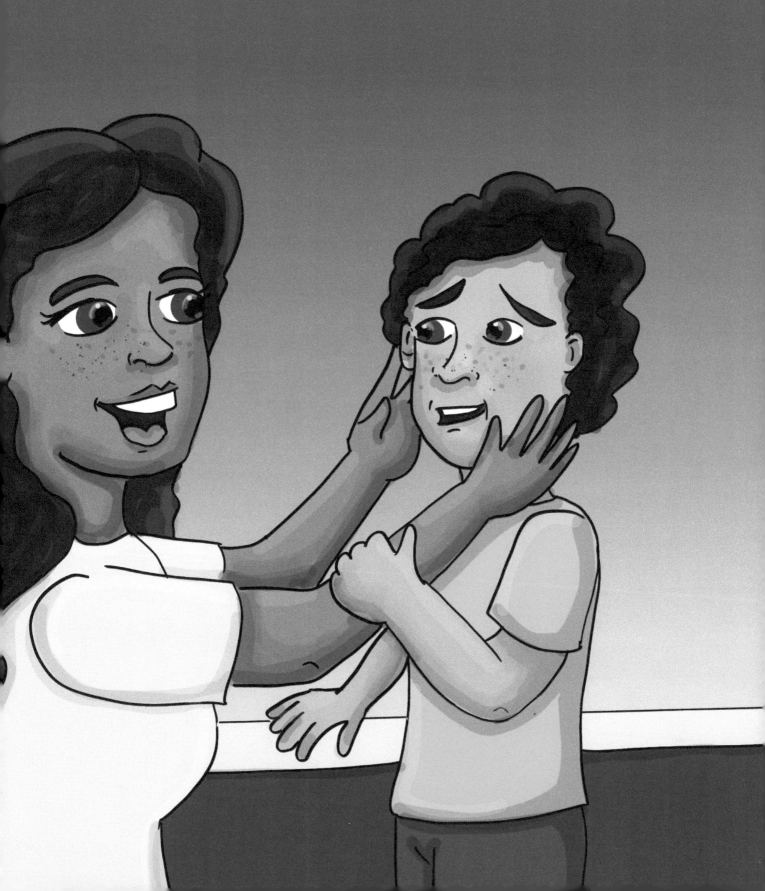

Today we are putting pictures and memories and drawings of us in a scrapbook.

It's good to remember the fun we had together. I know Daddy loved me. I will always miss him, but I know Mom and me will be okay.

For Adults
Now what?

Dear Parents and Guardians,

Thank you for purchasing this book for your child/children. Please be encouraged—you are doing the best possible job of being a good parent. We know it's never easy, but it is always worth it.

As you help your child through the grief process, be aware that children's process can differ from how adults process grief. You may notice they are acting out in unusual behaviors, such as getting angry or irritated easily. They may experience regression which could include not wanting to sleep alone, extreme attachment issues, bedwetting, lying, mood swings or anxiety.

Please try not to get angry, but instead talk to them about their feelings, thoughts and behaviors. Encourage them to journal or draw their feelings. It may be necessary to place them in individual therapy or group therapy in order for them to normalize through this time. Remember there is not a set time frame for healing from a parent's death. Please be patient and supportive.

Also, remember to take care of yourself during this time. You are equally important.

Sincerely,
Leticia A. Murphy, M.A., LMFT
Sharon D. Walling